Spring Fever

Michel Bridenne

ANGUS
& ROBERTSON
PUBLISHERS

ANGUS & ROBERTSON PUBLISHERS

Unit 4, Eden Park, 31 Waterloo Road,
North Ryde, NSW, Australia 2113, and
16 Golden Square, London W1R 4BN,
United Kingdom

First published in France
by Editions J. Glenat in 1984
First published in Australia
by Angus & Robertson Publishers in 1985
First published in the United Kingdom
by Angus & Robertson (UK) Ltd in 1985

ISBN 0 207 15046 X

Printed in Tokyo, Japan

To Brigitte Bardot

Michel Bridenne

Michel Bridenne

Michel Bridenne

Michel Bridenne

Michel Medenne

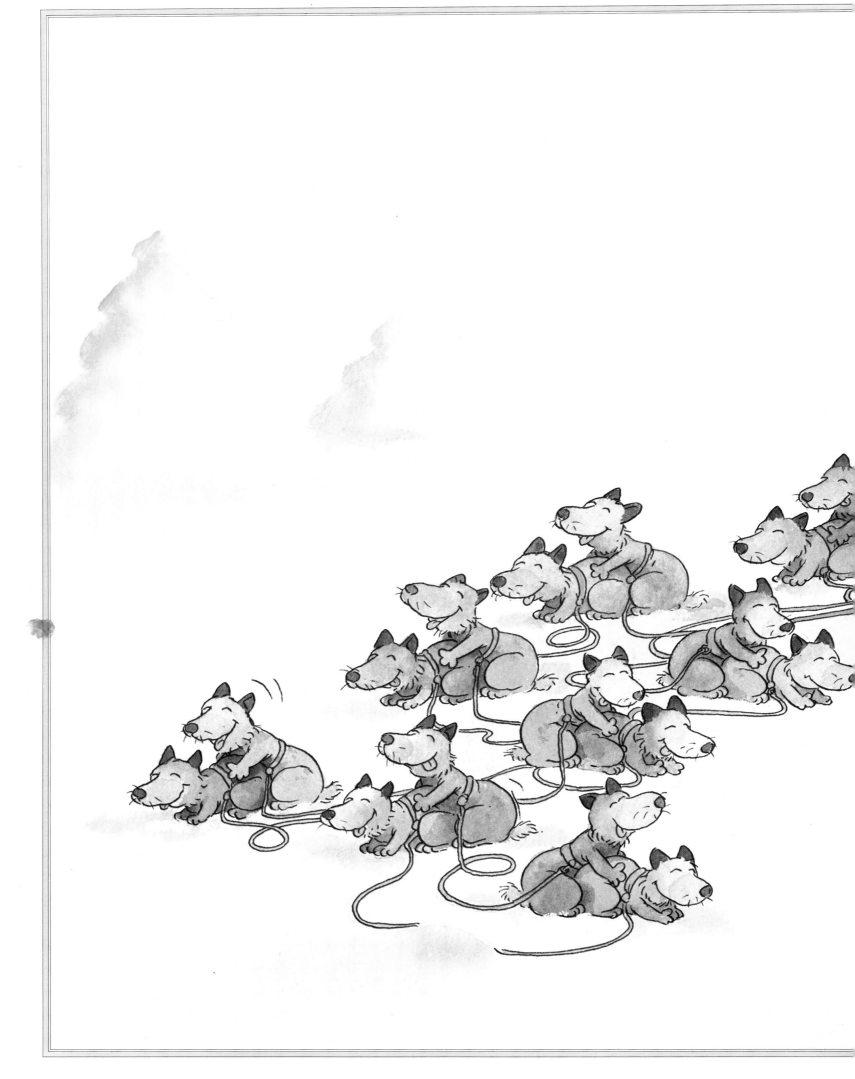

Michel Bridenne

Michel Bridenne

Michel Bridenne

Michel Bridenne